TRAIN WHISTLES

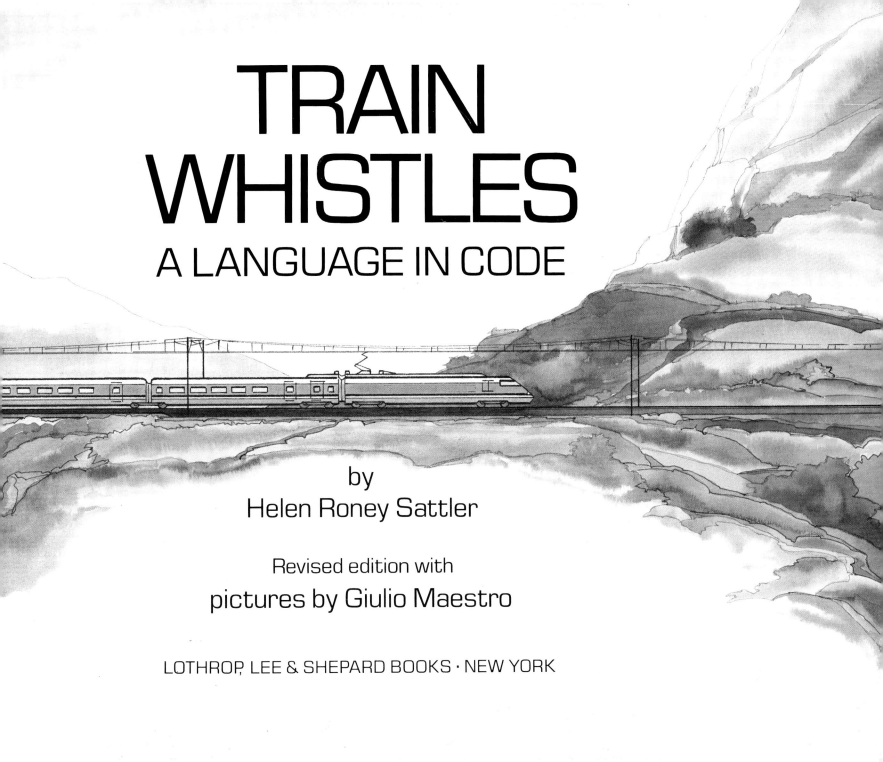

TRAIN WHISTLES
A LANGUAGE IN CODE

by

Helen Roney Sattler

Revised edition with

pictures by Giulio Maestro

LOTHROP, LEE & SHEPARD BOOKS · NEW YORK

With special thanks to Robert W. O'Brien, Director of Corporate Relations, Illinois Central Gulf Railroad,

for reading and checking the text and illustrations of this revised edition for accuracy.

Library of Congress Cataloging in Publication Data. Sattler, Helen Roney. Train whistles. Summary: Describes the use of train whistles as signals and what some of these signals mean. 1. Railroads—Signaling—Juvenile literature. 2. Locomotive sounds—Juvenile literature. [1. Railroads—Signaling. 2. Locomotives] I. Maestro, Giulio, ill. II. Title.   TF625.S27 1985   625.1'65 84-11279   ISBN 0-688-03978-2   ISBN 0-688-03980-4 (lib. bdg.)

TRAIN WHISTLES

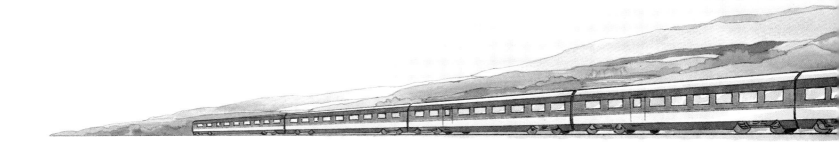

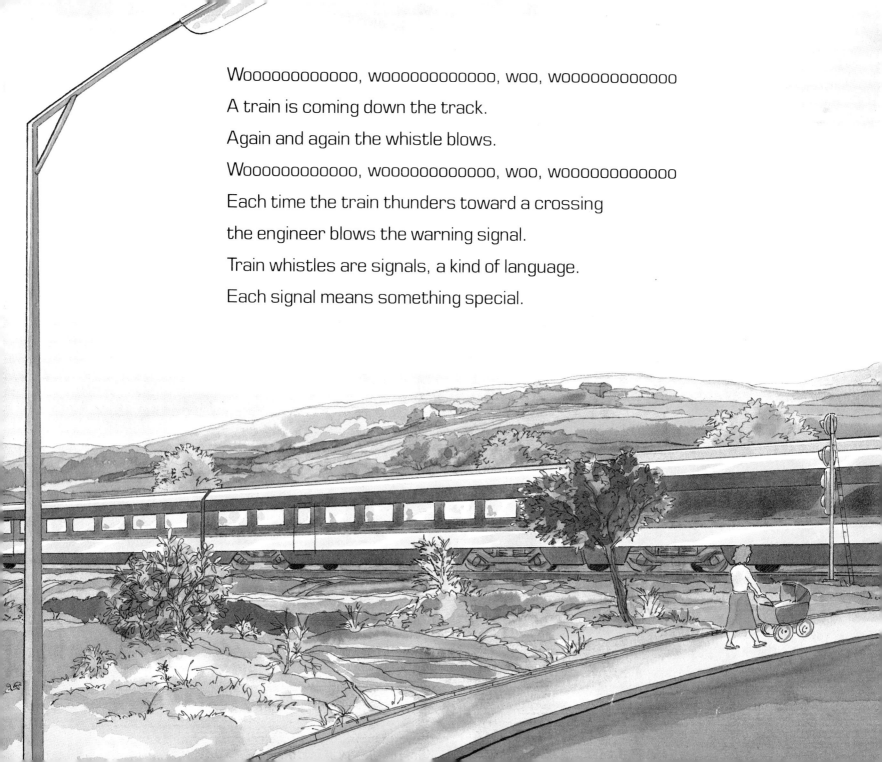

Woooooooooooo, wooooooooooo, woo, wooooooooooo

A train is coming down the track.

Again and again the whistle blows.

Woooooooooooo, wooooooooooo, woo, wooooooooooo

Each time the train thunders toward a crossing

the engineer blows the warning signal.

Train whistles are signals, a kind of language.

Each signal means something special.

Two long blasts, a short, and a long—mean,

"Stop, cars and people! Wait until the train has passed!"

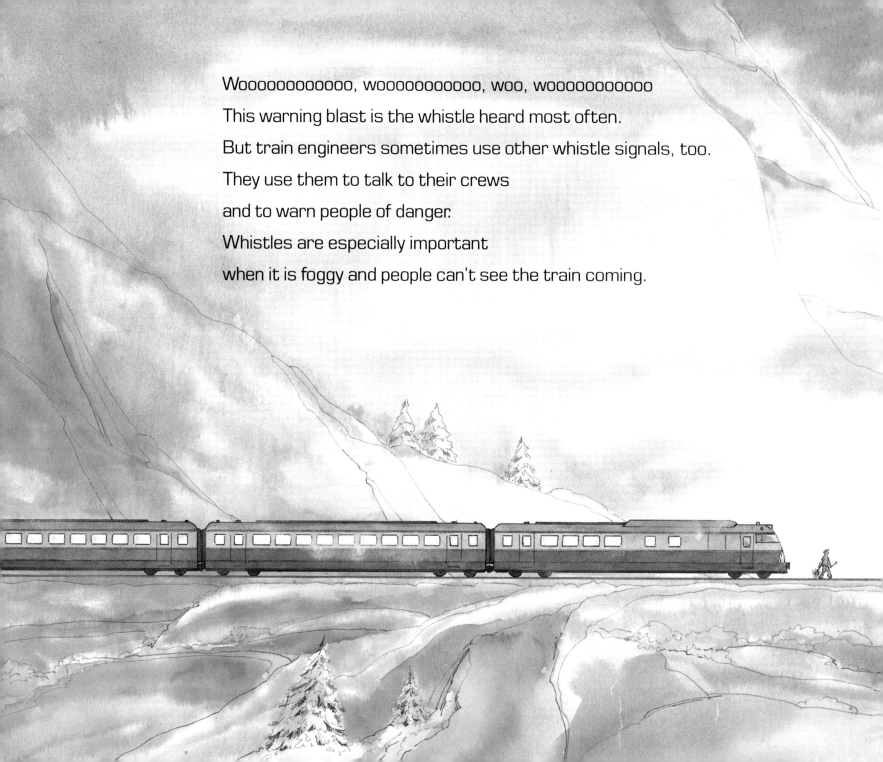

Woooooooooooo, wooooooooooo, woo, wooooooooooo

This warning blast is the whistle heard most often.

But train engineers sometimes use other whistle signals, too.

They use them to talk to their crews

and to warn people of danger.

Whistles are especially important

when it is foggy and people can't see the train coming.

On most modern railroads

train crews talk to each other by radio or telephone.

They use lights and electronic signals, too.

But on some trains, whistles are still used to give messages

and warnings to train workers who cannot

be reached in any other way.

This freight train will use many whistle signals
before it reaches its last stop.
Behind its two locomotives a long line of cars
play follow-the-leader:
coal cars, ore cars, flatcars, piggyback cars,
refrigerator cars, auto rack cars, cattle cars, boxcars,
tank cars, and covered hopper cars.

Last comes the caboose.

The conductor, who is boss of the train,

keeps the train's records in this tiny office on wheels.

A flagman helps watch for trouble

from the little windows on top.

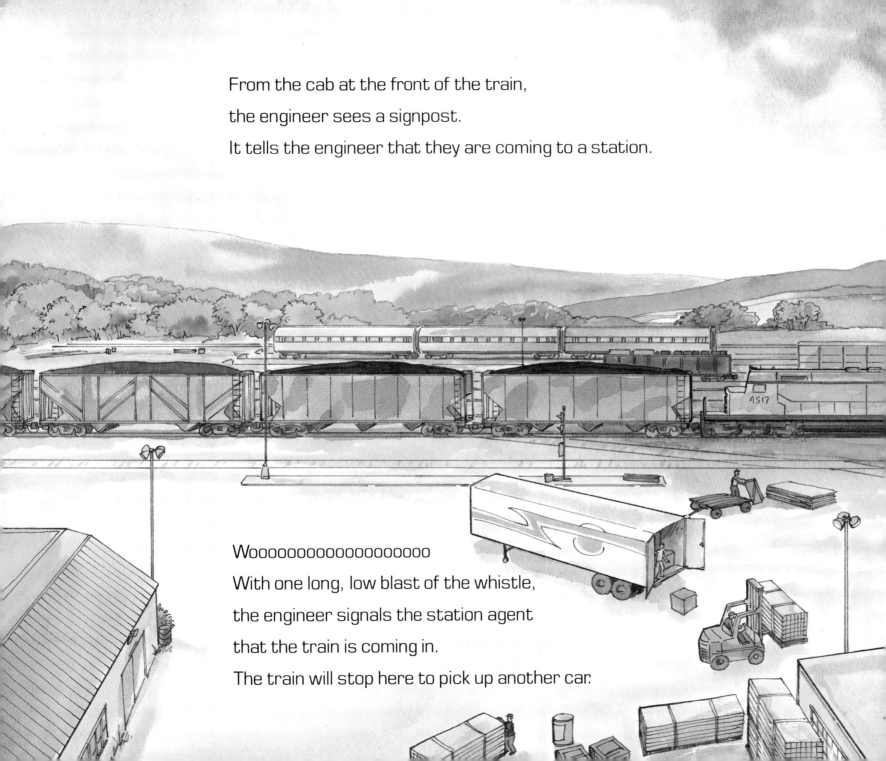

From the cab at the front of the train,
the engineer sees a signpost.
It tells the engineer that they are coming to a station.

Woooooooooooooooooooooo
With one long, low blast of the whistle,
the engineer signals the station agent
that the train is coming in.
The train will stop here to pick up another car.

Ding, ding, ding, ding, ding, ding, ding, ding
The engineer rings the bell to warn
everyone to keep off the tracks—
the train is still moving.

Shssssssssssssssssh go the air brakes,
screeeeeeeeeeeeech go the wheels on the track,
and clangity-bang! Freight cars bump together
as the train brakes to a stop.

Before the engineer backs the train
to couple on the new car,
he gives three short blasts on the whistle.
Toot, toot, toot
"Watch out!" it says. "The train is going to back up."

When the caboose is hooked on again
the train is ready to leave the station.
The engineer signals with two short whistle blasts:
Toot, toot
"Look out!" it warns. "This train is starting to move."

As the train speeds down the rails,
the engineer sees something on the track.
A cow? No, it is a deer!

The engineer blows the whistle again and again.

Toot, toot, toot, toot, toot, toot, toot, toot, toot

"Get off!" the whistle warns.

"Get off the track or you will get hurt!"

Now the train comes to a junction.

The engineer wants to know if the track ahead is clear.

Toot, toot, toot, toot

With four short blasts of the whistle,

he asks the operator to give him a signal.

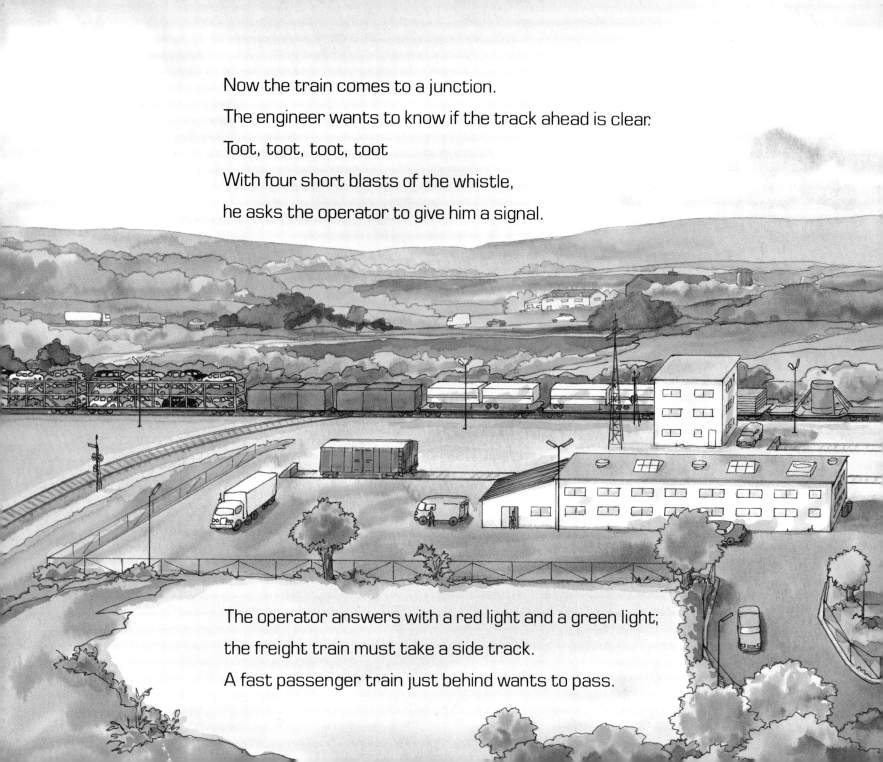

The operator answers with a red light and a green light;

the freight train must take a side track.

A fast passenger train just behind wants to pass.

One long, wailing note of the express train's whistle
signals that the train is passing through.
Woooooooooooooooooooooooooo
Without stopping, it speeds down the track
to some faraway city.

Only a few cars fly behind the locomotive—
baggage car, day coaches, dining car, sleeping cars,
lounge cars, and observation car.
Children wave as the express roars past
the freight train.

Back on the main track once more,

the freight train will soon reach a switchyard in a big city.

There its cars will be sorted and made up into new trains.

As the train nears the city,

the engineer receives a radio message.

There is danger ahead.

Rock has fallen onto the track.

The engineer stops the train
and blows the whistle to signal the rear flagman
to protect the rear of the train.
Wooooooooooooo, woo, woo, woo
One long and three short blasts send the flagman
down the track with a red flag and red flares.
The flares will warn all trains following them
that the freight train has stopped on the track.

A railroad crew soon clears away the fallen rock.

Then they check the track to be sure it is safe.

Now the train can run again.

The engineer calls in the flagman.

Woooooooooooo, woooooooooooo, woooooooooooo, woooooooooooo

Four long blasts of the whistle mean,

"Come on back, we're ready to go."

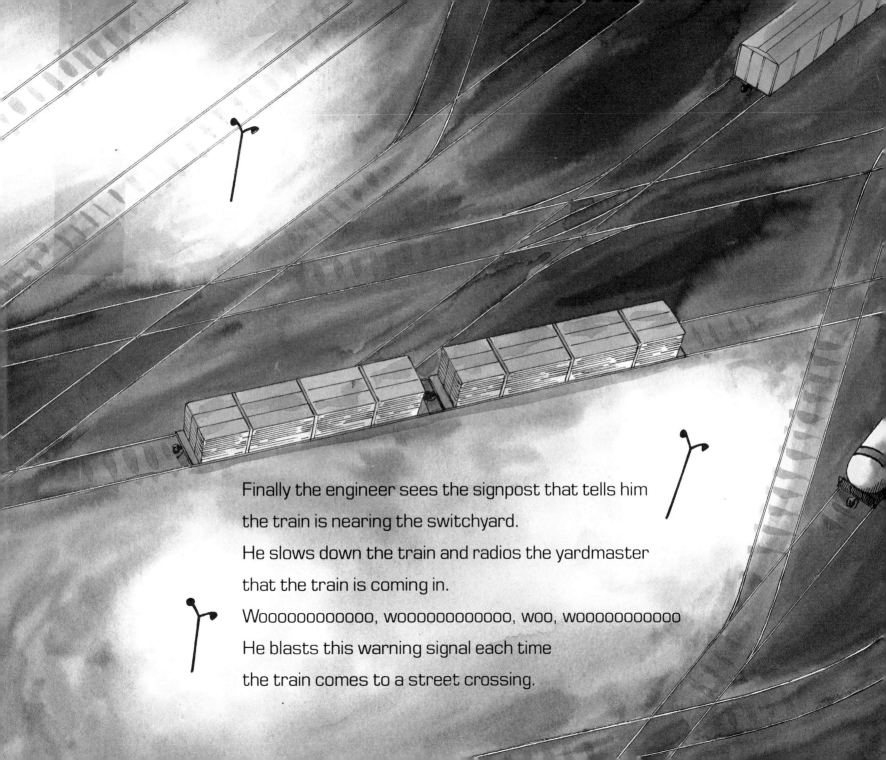

Finally the engineer sees the signpost that tells him
the train is nearing the switchyard.
He slows down the train and radios the yardmaster
that the train is coming in.
Wooooooooooooo, woooooooooooo, woo, wooooooooooo
He blasts this warning signal each time
the train comes to a street crossing.

Train whistles are not used as often now as they once were,
but they are still important warning signals
for people working near, or crossing over, tracks.

The next time you hear a train whistle, listen carefully.

Those blasts are more than noise—they are a message in code.

See if you can figure out what they are saying.

TRAIN WHISTLES IN THIS BOOK

HOW IT SOUNDS	WHAT IT MEANS
Two long blasts, one short, one long	To cars and people, STOP! The train is coming to a street crossing.
One long blast	The train is coming to a station or rail crossing.
Three short blasts (when standing)	The train is about to back up.
Two short blasts	Watch out! The train is starting to move.
Repeated short blasts	Get off the tracks.
Four short blasts	Give me a signal.
One long blast, three short	Rear flagman, protect the rear of the train.
Four long blasts	Flagman to the west or south, return to the train.

SOME OTHER TRAIN WHISTLES

Five long blasts	Flagman to the east or north, return to the train.
One short blast	To another train, STOP! There's something you don't see.
Three short blasts (when running)	Stop at the next station.
Two long blasts	Release brakes and proceed.

These are the most common signals. There are many others, and the meanings of some signals vary from one railroad company to another. Whatever the differences in meaning, all train whistles are a language in code.

625.1
SAT

Sattler, Helen Ro-
ney

Train whistles

DATE DUE

MAY 30 '86	DEC 0 2 '88	MAY 7 90	
SEP 26 '86	JAN 3 2 '90		
NOV 18 '86	DG 12 89		
JAN 7 '87	MAR 8 '90		
JAN 21 '87	AP 21 '90		
NOV 10 '87			
DEC 18 '87			
MAY 27 '88	JAN 27 92		
SEP 30 '88			
DEC 0 2 '88